HIGHLAND & CLOVER

imprint of Uitgeverij Hoogland & Van Klaveren

Original title: *Sagoresan - Från Junibacken till Nangilima*
Translated by: Frances Corry
© 2006 Text: Astrid Lindgren, c/o Saltkråkan AB, Stockholm
© 2006 Pictures, Foreword and Afterword: Marit Törnqvist
© 2010 Uitgeverij Hoogland & Van Klaveren
Printed by Drukkerij Slinger, The Netherlands
ISBN 978 90 8967 064 9

Astrid Lindgren & Marit Törnqvist

The Story Journey

FROM JUNEDALE TO NANGILIMA

HIGHLAND & CLOVER

PHOTO: LARS GRÖNWALL

The year was 1996. For three weeks, every morning at eight o'clock, I bicycled to Dalagatan 46 in Stockholm with a box of cream cakes on the luggage carrier. Astrid Lindgren was then 89 years old, and was writing what would be her last text, for the Story Train at Junibacken ("Junedale").

Two years earlier, I had been given the commission to create a three-dimensional story world based on six of Astrid's best loved books. The idea was that I would design scenes from the books, and monitor the construction of the entire scenography which was to be built on Djurgården in Stockholm. It was to be one thousand square metres, and seven metres tall. My head spun! Now, fifty of the best decorative craftsmen in Sweden were in the process of creating the story world I had designed.

Astrid alone could be the natural tour guide on the train, which was to bring the visitors through the stage sets. This was why I was visiting her every day. We read together from Emil and Karlsson and all the other books, and I described what the visitors would see from the Story Train. We studied my drawings with a magnifying glass, and I experienced how Astrid slowly but surely found the right tone for the Story Train script. A tone that melded with the books, with my drawings and with the experience that children and adults would have when travelling on the train.

I believe that Astrid enjoyed these sessions, "being busy with work" once again. And it felt as if we two together were on our own story journey, from Junedale to Nangilima.

Marit Törnqvist

This is Astrid Lindgren's script for the Story Train:

Hello, all you children!

Now we are off on a little trip to visit some other children, whom I think you may already know.

Mardie and Lisbet who lived in Junedale, you've heard about them, haven't you?

Do you remember when they had an outing and Mardie jumped off the roof of the wood-shed and nearly killed herself?

Abe made up all kinds of crazy stories. Like the night when he persuaded Mardie to go into the washhouse, and pretended to be a ghost.

Now we come to Katthult, where Emil lived. And look, there's Alfred!
   It was Sunday, and they were having a party at Katthult. People were on their way to the party, and the flag was up the pole. Haha, that's what you thought! It was little Ida, whom Emil had run up the flagpole. So it was the toolshed for Emil as usual, after one of his pranks.

Suddenly they found that Emil had disappeared.
Oh, how they searched for him everywhere.
But there was no sign of Emil, for Emil had moved out of the toolshed…
…and over to the foodstore. And there, if you please, he lay down and went
to sleep in a cupboard with a lot of sausage skins scattered around him.

Another party that everybody in Lönneberga were talking about for a long
time was the one given by Emil on Boxing Day. He invited all the poor
hungry people from the workhouse to come to Katthult and eat their fill.
He had a good heart, that Emil!

Have you noticed that we are flying?
  And those lights down there, that must be Vasastan
in Stockholm. And Midge's house. He is probably
down there, waiting for Karlsson as usual.

Karlsson is a handsome, intelligent and reasonably stout man in his prime, and he flies in when he likes.

Karlsson lives in a little house on the roof. And here it is! Oh dear, oh dear, what a mess! We don't want to stop here.

But what has happened to us now? We have become as small as Simon Small himself. He was no bigger than a thumb, and he lived under the floor under Bertil's bed. He rented a flat there from a horrid rat.

Bertil wanted to be as small as Simon, so that they could play together.

It's fun to be so small that you can bathe in a sugarbowl.

Oh, what a storm!
And we are in the middle of a great forest.
This is Matt's forest, where Matt's robbers
hang out ...

… where treacherous grey dwarves live behind the boulders and rumphobs beneath the roots of the trees. And there are Ronja and Birk, too. They have moved to the Bears' Cave to get some peace, and escape from the row between Matt's robbers and Borka's robbers.

Matt's robbers were standing beside Hell's Gap, furious
because Borka's robbers had moved into the fort without
permission.

But in the end they became friends, and when spring
came at last, Ronja yelled her old spring yell for joy.

But what's going on here?

   There's a fire! This was where Jonathan took his sick
little brother on his back and jumped out of the window.

   There was no more Jonathan. He died when he jumped
out, and poor Rusky was left alone.

   But one evening, a snow-white dove flew up and perched
on the window ledge, and Rusky knew, at once, that it was
Jonathan.

Jonathan had talked about a place called Nangiyala, where you went when you were dead. And Rusky went there too, to Cherry Valley in Nangiyala. Jonathan was sitting there, fishing. Imagine Rusky's joy!

But in Nangiyala, there was also Wild Rose Valley, which was no longer free. It was ruled over by cruel Tengil, and his even more cruel dragon, Katla. But a nice old grandfather, Mattias, lived there too. Jonathan and Rusky hid in his house until it was time to set out for Tengil's country.

Their journey led across the bridge over the terrifying Karma Falls. And it was there, for the first time, that they saw Katla, the she-dragon from ancient times.

Then came the great final battle, which set Wild Rose Valley free again, but by then Jonathan had already been paralysed by Katla's fire.

As they rested by the precipice that plunged straight down into the depths, Jonathan talked about Nangilima, and how wonderful it was there.

Then Rusky took his brother on his back and jumped over the edge, into the lights of Nangilima.

A journey through Astrid Lindgren's worlds

Astrid Lindgren's stories are some of my first memories. Mummy, who was Astrid's Dutch translator, read all her books to us children. This has had a great influence on what happened later.

When I was eight years old, my parents bought an old farmstead in Småland, in southern Sweden. We used to go there in the summer, in autumn, in winter and in spring. Our neighbours, two siblings, had a working farm where I helped out every day. An old-fashioned farm, where the farmwife still called the cows in the forest with a pretty melody, where hay was piled on the old-fashioned drying racks, where food was cooked on a wood-fired iron stove. I took part in the sewing circle with my small piece of knitting. The priest played the organ and read aloud to all the old ladies. And the old ladies drank their coffee off the saucer, with a lump of sugar clamped between their lips. I was quite convinced that Småland would become my future; I would take over the farm and become a farmer.

In a way, Småland did become my future, but thanks to another place where I also used to spend many hours every day, the cabin where the farm-hands had used to live. Here, my siblings and I did woodwork, painted and built enormous landscapes and dolls' houses – landscapes with lakes and rivers and caves, dolls' houses with furniture, china services, curtains, wallpaper and a complete larder filled with food; all made from wood, fabric and clay.

Now it sounds like Sweden was my life, but I really lived in Holland. My friends there had never seen a toolshed like Emil's, or an ancient forest like Ronja's, or even tasted a cinnamon bun like Karlsson's. But they loved Astrid's books, just like I did.

Perhaps it is not so strange that, with this background, I became a children's book illustrator. After finishing at the Academy of Art in Amsterdam, my first commission was to make a picture book of the story "When the Bäckhult farmer went to town", which Astrid had written in the 1950s. Now I had the chance to paint my longing for Sweden and the Småland snow landscape as I sat there in the Dutch drizzle. And it was as if Astrid's childhood memories and my own melded together.

The strange thing was that my documentation was hardly done in any library, but among my Småland neighbours. In their wardrobes, I found clothes that their parents had worn, their cupboards held old china and their heads were full of information about how people lived in Småland in around 1910.

Later, I did several picture books for Astrid, at the same time as I did illustrations for many Dutch authors and also started writing myself.

But it was thanks to the picture books with Astrid's texts that Staffan Götestam came looking for me in 1994 and commissioned me to create the story journey at Junibacken.

To begin with, I was a bit doubtful. Why were they building a story journey out of Astrid's fantastic works? Were the books not enough as they were? My doubts also concerned the train. Why was the audience not allowed to move at its own pace? But fairly quickly I realized that only with the train would it be possible to bring big and little people on a dream-like journey, where light, sound and movement could be adapted to each other, where I myself could determine sightlines and eye levels. No glass windows would be needed to protect the décor.

Despite all my doubts, I chose to take the step and join the great project. The starting point was a rough model showing the route of the cable way. The commission was to make room for six of Astrid's books. The rest I had to fill in myself.

A boarding station and a carriage were the first bits I had to imagine, and it was obvious to me to start with Vimmerby station, as it would have looked when Astrid was young. In a small wooden carriage, which also existed in those days, the audience would be ferried from the more realistic books about Mardie and Emil in Småland to Stockholm and the "semi-realistic" Karlsson on the Roof and Simon Small, and finally to the folktale-like worlds of Ronja and the Brothers Lionheart.

I used the techniques of film-making, by changing the scale of the stage sets and the height and angle of the carriage as needed.

For instance, it was important that we in

the cable carriage, just like Karlsson, could fly high above Vasastan. For this reason, 240 small-scale houses were built, to contrast with Karlsson's, which had to look as realistic as possible with all of Karlsson's strange belongings in natural scale.

When I did my drawings, I was always careful not to show the main characters too clearly, in order not to collide with earlier interpretations. Emil sleeping in a dark cupboard, Birk and Ronja as silhouettes against the camp fire, and Simon Small sitting deep down in a sugar bowl. In this way, I hoped there was enough space for the children's own mental images.

All kinds of decorative craftsmen were contacted, from among others the Stockholm city theatre Stadsteatern, the Drottningholm Theatre, the Royal Dramatic Theatre and Filmhuset, the Swedish Film Institute. Their experience helped to translate my two-dimensional images into three-dimensional stage sets. We were constantly experimenting and searching for solutions, not least because of the practical regulations. The fire safety rules were so strict that the costume maker almost felt obliged to make all the clothes from sheet metal. Every day we came across surprises, such as an emergency exit or a fire escape in the middle of Ronja's fort or Emil's toolshed.

In the end, I worked with nearly 70 expert stage set craftsmen – tree makers, house carpenters, cliff sculptors, water moulders, cobblestone setters, landscape builders, makers of dolls, animals and dragons, and of course lighting experts. Some had 20 years of experience, while others were unemployed within their professions. But all had as their first task to re-read the books, so that they knew the stories they were telling.

We soon noticed that my paintings were not enough as precepts for the scene building. But if I said that Ronja belonged to the Viking era, and the Wild Rose Valley of the brothers Lionheart to the Swedish Middle Ages, then it became easier to understand the appearance and materials of the architecture and costumes.

As extra help, I handed out photographs of flowering cherry trees, Småland door handles, mossy single roof tiles, street lights and waterfalls. I travelled from southern Sweden to Lapland, taking photographs everywhere. Sometimes I bicycled around with mossy branches or black rocks on my luggage carrier, in order to show what I meant.

But although I did all this work, it was as if my craftsmen were training me to be a stage designer. They taught me all about different materials, how to build models and make builders' drawings. I had never held a scale rule in my hands before!

We worked night and day, because we were running out of money and time. We had chosen a fairly unusual route for a multimillion project: experimentation, small-scale work, personal inventions. My intuition told me that the most personal could become the most universal in the end.

The fact that this attitude sometimes collided with the management of Junibacken is not so surprising. Convincing them that every detail had to be made by hand, that no mass production of, for instance, dolls' hands was possible was not always so easy.

Letting the doll makers create an entire character, a farmer with horny hands, Mrs Petrell with pale, slender fingers and a lot of jewellery, this was really part of the joy of the work. Everybody worked their hearts out, with enormous feeling and empathy.

The only person who could be our guide on this story-like journey was, of course, Astrid. Every morning for several weeks, we sat together in her sofa and worked. We read the books and studied the illustrations carefully, and meanwhile the storyline wound its way and tied together all the adventures on the journey from Junedale to Nangilima. And finally Astrid was satisfied with her text. It was translated into all sorts of languages – my own mother read it in Dutch.

And then at last, on 8 June 1996, Junibacken was opened by the Swedish King and Queen. I took a trip on the train, and my mother read to me. Just like twenty-five years

Marit Törnqvist